Quentin Blake's
NURSERY RHYME BOOK

Jonathan Cape
Thirty Bedford Square London

Other books by Quentin Blake

PATRICK
JACK AND NANCY
ANGELO
SNUFF
MR MAGNOLIA

Illustrated by Quentin Blake

HOW TOM BEAT CAPTAIN NAJORK AND
HIS HIRED SPORTSMEN
text by Russell Hoban
A NEAR THING FOR CAPTAIN NAJORK
text by Russell Hoban
THE ENORMOUS CROCODILE
text by Roald Dahl
REVOLTING RHYMES
text by Roald Dahl

The author and publishers are grateful to
Oxford University Press for permission to use
the rhymes, some from Iona and Peter Opie's
Oxford Dictionary of Nursery Rhymes (1951)
and some from their *Oxford Nursery Rhyme
Book* (1955)

First published 1983
Illustrations © 1983 by Quentin Blake

Jonathan Cape Ltd, 30 Bedford Square, London WC1

British Library Cataloguing in Publication Data
Blake, Quentin
Quentin Blake's nursery rhyme book
1. Nursery rhymes, English
I. Title
398'.8   PZ8.3
ISBN 0 224 02144 3

Printed in Great Britain by
W.S. Cowell Ltd, Butter Market, Ipswich

Little Jack Sprat
  Once had a pig,
It was not very little,
  Nor yet very big,
It was not very lean,
  It was not very fat –
It's a good pig to grunt,
  Said little Jack Sprat.

Ickle ockle, blue bockle,
Fishes in the sea,

If you want a pretty maid,
Please choose me.

Jeremiah,
   blow the fire,
      Puff, puff, puff.

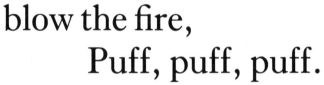

First you blow it gently

Then you blow it rough.

Handy spandy, Jack-a-Dandy
Loves plum cake and sugar candy.
He bought some at a
grocer's shop

And out he came,
    hop, hop,
        hop, hop!

Gregory Griggs,
Gregory Griggs,
Had twenty-seven
different wigs.

He wore them up,
he wore them down
To please the people
of the town;

He wore them east,
    he wore them west,
But he never could tell
    which he loved the best.

Dickery, dickery, dare,
The pig flew up in the air;

The man in brown
soon brought him down,
Dickery, dickery, dare.

I had a little husband
　　No bigger than my thumb;
I put him in a pint pot
　　And there I bid him drum.
I gave him some garters
　　To garter up his hose,
And a little silk handkerchief
　　To wipe his pretty nose.

Pussy Cat ate the dumplings,
Pussy Cat ate the dumplings,
Mama stood by,
And cried, Oh, fie!
Why did you eat
the dumplings?

William McTrimbletoe,
  He's a good fisherman,

Catches fishes

Puts them in dishes,

Catches hens
  Puts them in pens,

Some lay eggs

Some lay none

William McTrimbletoe,
He doesn't eat one.

Pretty John Watts,
We are troubled with rats,
Will you drive them out of the house?

We have mice, too, in plenty
That feast in the pantry,
But let them stay,
And nibble away:
What harm is a little brown mouse?

Little Blue Ben,
who lives in the glen,
Keeps a blue cat
and one blue hen

Which lays of blue eggs
          a score and ten;
Where shall I find
          the little Blue Ben?

Goosey, goosey gander,
Who stands yonder?
Little Betsy Baker;

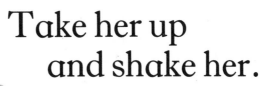

Take her up
and shake her.

Terence McDiddler,

The three-stringed fiddler,

Can charm, if you please,

The fish from the seas!

Robin the Bobbin
the big-bellied Ben
He ate more meat
than fourscore men.

He ate a cow
he ate a calf
He ate a butcher
and a half

He ate a church
   he ate a steeple
He ate a priest
   and all the people

A cow and a calf
A butcher and a half
A church and a steeple
And all the good people

And yet he complained
   that his stomach wasn't
      full.

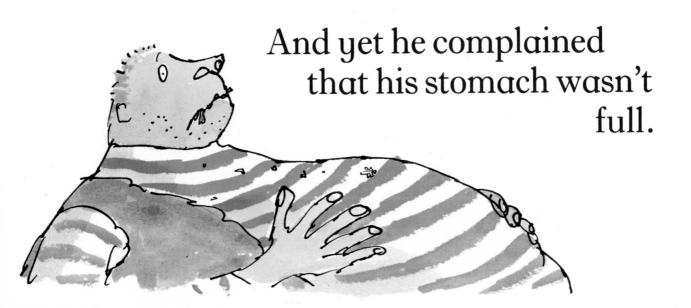

Here am I
Little Jumping Joan;

When nobody's with me
I'm all alone.

Oh, Mother,
I shall be married
to Mr Punchinello,

To Mr Punch,
To Mr Joe,
To Mr Nell,
To Mr Lo,

Mr Punch, Mr Joe,
Mr Nell, Mr Lo,
To Mr Punchinello!